The**Oldie**

Book of Cartoons

The **Oldie**

Book of Cartoons

CHOSEN BY RICHARD INGRAMS

Park McDonald
London

This compilation first published by Park McDonald in 1995
Reprinted 1996

Copyright © 1995 Oldie Publications Ltd

The publishers would like to thank the respective copyright owners for
permission to include illustrations in this volume

Park McDonald is an imprint of
Deirdre McDonald Books
7 Westhorpe Road
London SW15 1QH

A CIP catalogue record for this book is available from the British Library

ISBN 1 898094 13 6

Printed and bound in Great Britain by Biddles Ltd

Introduction

Since starting *The Oldie* in 1992 I have been delighted by the response we have had from the nation's cartoonists.

Despite the paucity of the remuneration (due to limited funds) the cartoons have flooded in from all over the country.

Some of them have come from names familiar to me from long years on *Private Eye*, a few I recognize from the old days of *Punch* (now, sadly, no longer with us).

But many are completely new to me and also, I'm sure, to my readers.

To all of them many thanks for providing such a varied assortment.

RICHARD INGRAMS

*Our thanks to the following cartoonists
whose work is represented herein:*

Sally Artz, David Austin, Brian Bagnall, Nick Baker, Les Barton, Bill Belcher, Doug Bennett,
Neil Bennett, Philip Berkin, Hugh Burnett, Ray Chesterton, Cluff, Peter Cooper,
Keith Courtney, George Craig, Jon Cramer, Mike Darling, Alan Davies, Alan de la Nougerede,
Neil Dishington, M. Donohue, Nick Downes, Sean Doyle, Pete Dredge, Pat Drennan,
Frank Finch, David Haldane, David Hawker, Trevor Heaton, William Hewison, Martin Honeysett,
Jim Hunter, Tony Husband, Ionicus, Richard Jolley, Gray Jolliffe, Jorodo, Ham Khan,
Barry Knowles, Kathryn Lamb, David Langdon, Larry, Edward McLachlan, Kieran Meehan,
Nicolette Meeres, Ged Melling, P. D. Moulson, Roy Nixon, Richard Orchard, Pantelis Palios,
Peji, J. Pugh, Ken Pyne, Derek Rains, Bryan Reading, Bill Round, William Scully, Stan Seed, Sewell,
Adam Singleton, George Smith, Sam Smith, Anthony Spittle, Carol Stokes,
Gordon Stowell, P. Taylor, Geoff Thompson, Robert Thompson, Bill Tidy, Richard Tomes,
Mike Turner, Geoff Waterhouse, Steve Way, Bob Wilson, Paul Wood and Kevin Woodcock.

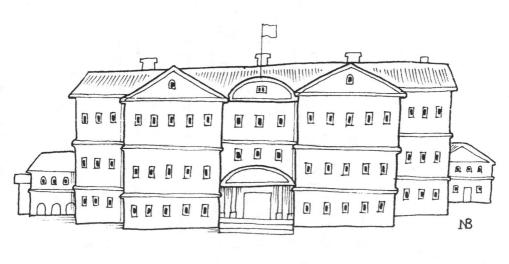

'It's just an ordinary 300 up, 300 down'

'I'm sorry I don't have any form of identification.
Isn't being your husband enough?'

'I think I'll check in on how Bob's presentation went'

'His behaviour is too damned courteous –
I suspect he's been drinking'

9

'Not guilty, Fred'

*'I'd stop you, but I'm afraid TV has numbed me to
the impact of dramatic, real-life events'*

'To think that less than a month ago you were merely
a phone number among the graffiti'

Waterhouse

'Good news, sir – someone's stolen the Hockney'

'Mum, Dad – this is Kevin. Kevin works in advertising'

'My name is Harry Brown and I am an exhibitionist...'

'Nice tits!'

'You're very quiet tonight, dear'

'I think these wild rumours that the company is controlled by some mysterious cult must be squelched immediately, O High Priest of Utter Darkness'

'Let me through! I'm a ghoul!'

'Agnes is leaving me for someone with more air miles'

'Polonius, do you mind if I give you
a damn good kicking first – we've got a
bus load of football fans in'

'You're quite safe – I'm not an MP or anything like that…'

M'LUD   KATHRYN LAMB

M'LUD'S DECIDED TO
CUT THROUGH LEGAL JARGON
AND REACH OUT TO THE YOUTH
OF TODAY

LAWS 'Я' US

'Did you say this was your first christening?'

'He's at a meeting'

'Don't be silly, dear, there'll be other crusades'

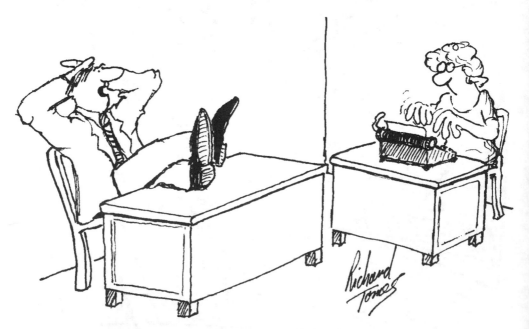

'... or I'll tear your head off and sell the rest of you for dog food.
Yours affectionately... '

'But you're not losing a daughter, we're going to live here'

'Here's one I made earlier...'

'What time would you like the cockerel to wake you in the morning?'

'Mr Noah? We're from the Council Planning Department'

'I forget. Are we Aztecs or Incas?'

'…£150,000… Sold to the gentleman in the Napoleon uniform with a banana stuck in his ear'

'That one cost me an arm and a leg in '63'

'Today we did coitus interruptus…'

'You mean we get to choose?'

'I had that Rolf Harris in my cab
this morning'

...in tonight's programme,
children, we'll be showing you how to
embalm that dead pet...

'One-day Rover'

'And they say that women Mary's age stand as much chance of
getting married as being taken hostage by a terrorist'

'Benson, pass His Lordship the soap'

'Woof, Woof!'

'You pays your money and you takes your Joyce'

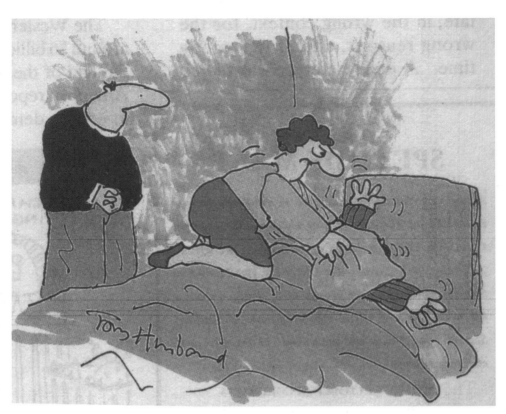

'That doesn't look much like voluntary euthanasia to me, Mrs Forbes'

'Gerald's frightfully clever. He's won a place in an open prison'

'Sorry I'm late, I overslept'

'Hang on, that can't be right'

'We'll see if there isn't something we can't get you for the pain'

*'How do you plead... framed
or not framed?'*

*'Don't worry, madam, I'll soon
get him down for you'*

'Me and the Merry Men think you're spending too much time on the paperwork, Robin'

'*I wish to enrol for the chattering classes*'

'*He has an unfortunate manner…*'

'It's the inscription on Dad's tombstone. He won't let Mum put "miserable, tight-fisted old bastard"'

'Get much huntin' between books?'

'And here's one I made earlier…'

HUNTER

'No, Joe! Not through there – it's a trompe l'oeil… !'

'Blimey, you're early. Hang on and I'll be with you in a bit'

'Who's next wealthiest?'

'Very sad… He was a sniffer for the Met'

'I want my pudding to go to Sarajevo'

'George, do you mind if we don't have the puppet show tonight? I'm so tired'

'Hang on! Somebody's not cheating!'

'We're unable to reach a verdict, m'lud. Three nights
in a luxury hotel might help us...'

'Actually it's my wife – I wonder if you'd jump-start her out of her depression'

'What does he mean, "A pint of ordinary bitter"?'

'Here is a newspaper published on the very day he was born'

'I find you get much better coverage from the broadsheets'

'Is that a divertimento or is he just doing his party piece?'

'Those marked with an asterisk are served with bad humour'

'I think I'll wait for the paperback'

'It was on sale'

'You never spray
"I love you" any more'

'There's a message coming through – it says, "Sorry, he's at a meeting"…'

49

'It's that beastly man collecting for the RSPCA'

'Well, Marjorie, he still looks like a Nazi war criminal to me'

'Charles! Would we be interested in a trip to Mars?'

'Don't try anything or I'll sue you for resisting a burglary'

'I can't see the point of all these damn meetings'

'Love to stay, but I'm afraid our parking time has expired'

*'Well your employer's obliged
to give three weeks' notice before
drowning you'*

'Always legless that one!'

'I'm always the same. I don't know what to do in the country'

'He's getting a short, sharp, shock'

'Whose turn is it to start tonight's argument?'

*'Now you're getting older your confessions
are very, very boring!'*

'Bloody Germans!'

'All right, what's the first thing we check <u>after</u> the stereo being on full blast?'

'Mr Pontin! Have you been playing
tank battles again?'

'...I'm going to put you
on hold, sir. Do you prefer
middle of the road,
classical, jazz, heavy metal,
pop, country and western,
rap, spiritual...'

'I've got a job for you, Penbury – I want you to go out and look for one!'

'It's got a good buzz this place'

'I suppose if you really must have a second opinion – I could change my mind'

'Heinz or Campbells?'

'You'll have to excuse him, he's under a lot of atmospheric pressure at the moment'

'George writes travel books'

'I've called this meeting to decide if there's any point in holding a meeting'

'Powerful sermon, Reverend'

'I see the housing market is picking up'

'*Good morning, I'd like to talk to you about the Bible*'

'That one's shark-bait'

'I wonder if you could make love more quietly. My wife is starting to make unfavourable comparisons'

'Could you run that one by me again?'

'Harvey, have you electrified the bird-bath again?'

CRAMER.

ROBERT THOMPSON.

'On a clear day you can see the ground'

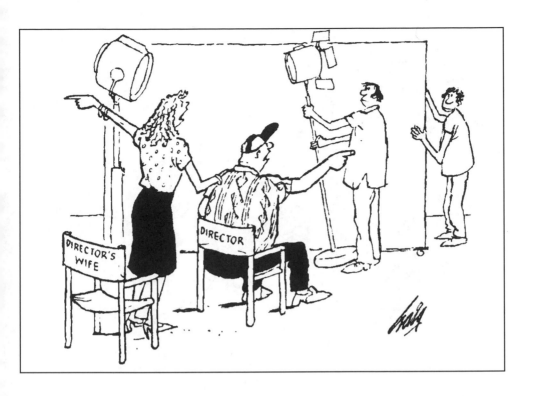

'A packet of salt 'n' vinegar crisps, barman, and have one for yourself!'

'It's from the police thanking me for
helping them with their enquiries'

'Looks like we're eating in
again tonight'

'I thought we came here to relax!'

'... and may I please have a pillow?'

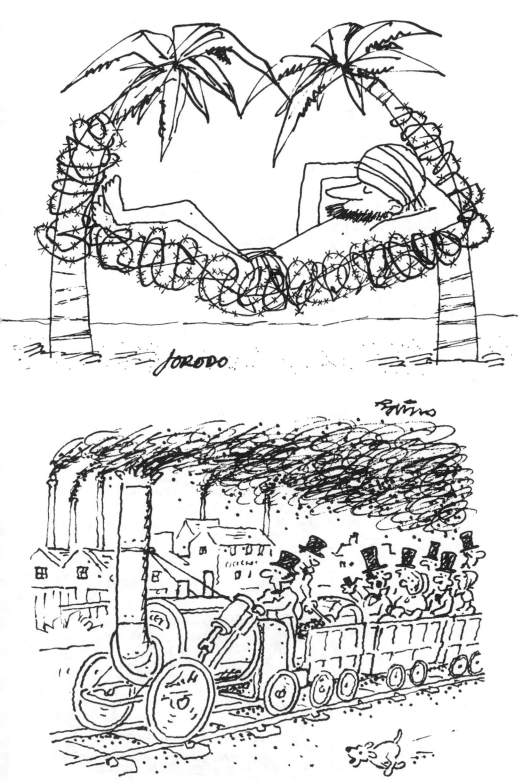

'Do you mind if I smoke?'

'Remind me – am I getting up or going to bed?'

Reading

'He used to be the doyen of something or other'

darling

'But the best thing about this coat, modom, is that it's real fur made up to look fake'

'You know what I miss? Telling Esther Rantzen to bugger off'

'Dinner is served!'

'Nigel persuaded his parents to move nearer so he could keep an eye on them'

'Don't start thinking about the Dordogne – our roots are here'

'Sorry, madam, we don't do people'

PICK THE RIGHT ONE AND WIN A FITTED KITCHEN

'It's the English cricket-test selectors'

Waterhouse

'I'm surprised you got custody of us, Dad'

'It's for you'

'Try and be a little less avant-garde, Mrs Groat'

'Well, at least we've synchronized our insomnia…'

'I have this nightmare that Jeffrey Bernard is my patient'

'Kindly use the middle management
ledge, Perkins!'

'Excuse me, do the Thatchers live round here?'

'Can I have a Filipino housemaid bag?'

'And was he always a keen
do-it-yourself man?'

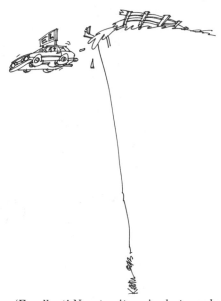

'Excellent! Now try it again, but maybe
a little earlier on the brake'

'You still have the fish shop then?'

'Bad news, I'm afraid you've only got 85 years to live!'

'I can't stand this foreign muck – gimme a pizza or a curry any day!'

'Marriages today seem to be over before they've begun'

'...and this is your blood-pressure warning light'

'Living gods don't wear zip-up cardis'

'Did you shut the conservatory door?'

'What year's the spring water?'

'This used to be a nice, quiet neighbourhood till that lot moved in'

'… and you must be Sleazy!'

'Unaccustomed as I am to public squeaking'

'Got any crisps potato flavour?'

'Ms Pemberton – bring me a copy of the Financial Times... *rolled up'*

'The paparazzi!'

'Eye of newt, wing of bat, …oh sod it, let's open a tin'

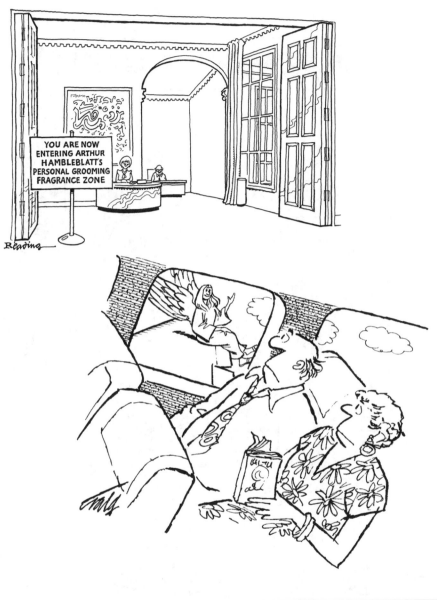

'Oh, goody! Here comes the swede trolley!'

'I've forgotten what my famous last words were going to be'

'And at the end of that round, Mr Bell,
you've proved that you're a sad little old man whose
only interest in life is Henry VIII'

'Can't this wait till Monday?'

'How many times, Tanya,
don't ring me at work'

'My wife doesn't understand my computer...'

'Look what I found in your old
tea-chest in the loft'

'I've decided to go for set-aside'

'He insists on having his
solicitor present!'

'Tyndale's not on till three – I'm just the warm-up act'